He puts on his jacket.

He sits in his buggy.

Clunk! Clunk!

Then off he goes
to Baby Club.

Everyone says 'Hello'.

First they sing the happy song.

Boo!

Then they play
peek-a boo!

Boo!

Stretch! Stretch!

They sing the stretchy song.

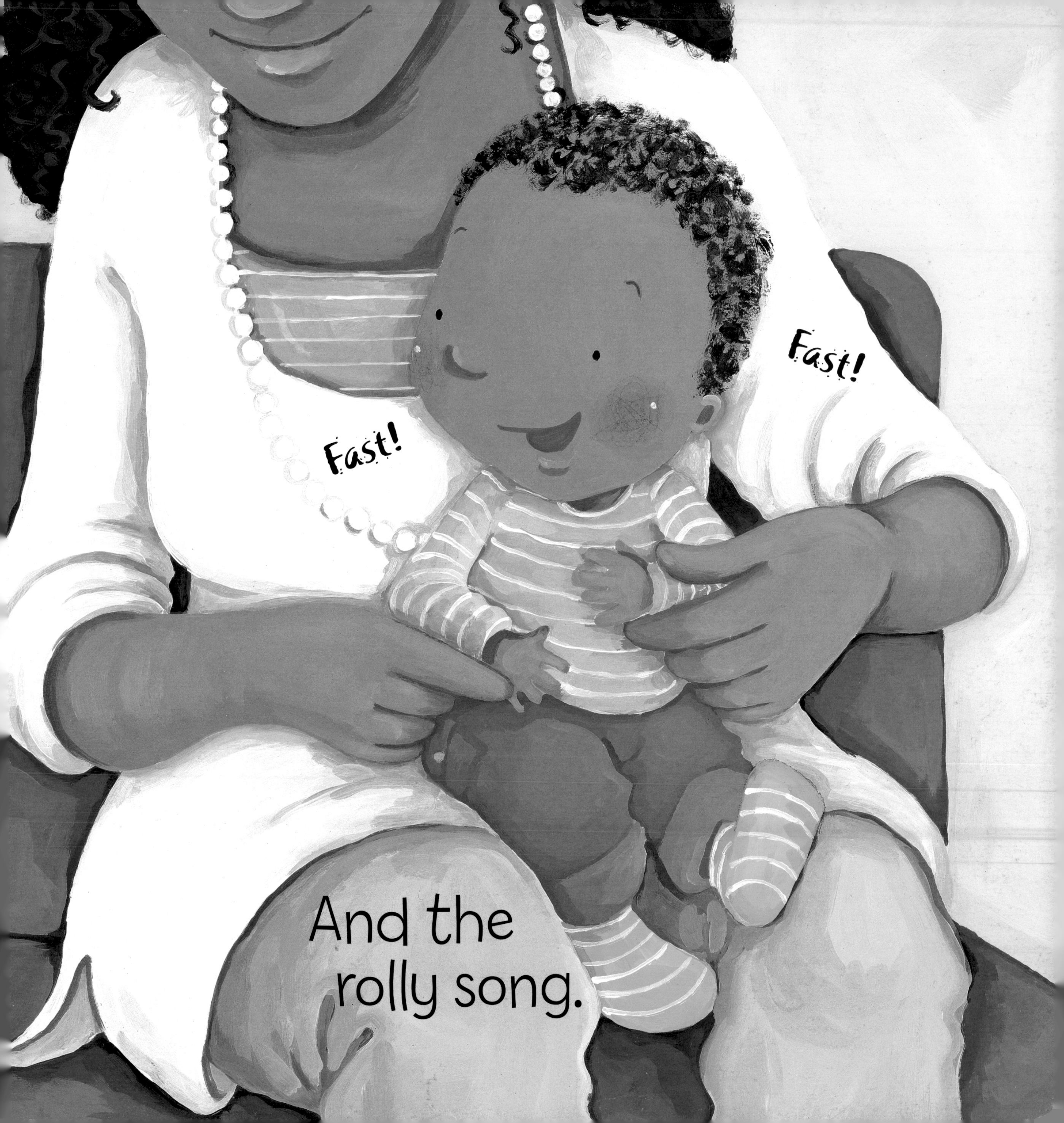

And the
rolly song.

Next they play
with their animals.

meow

woof

oink

That's Zeki's favourite!

They wiggle
their fingers

and clap
their hands.

They wave
their arms

and kick
their legs.

They ride the bus...

up!

down!

...and their horses!

giddy up!

Then they

Zooooooooooo

mmmm to the moooon!

Last, there's time for a cuddle, a story,

and making new friends.

bye!

ciao!
slán!
au revoir!

If You're Happy and You Know it!

This is a lovely song to start off with. You can add other actions if you like - we've added 'do an dance' in our Toddler Group and the little ones love to get up and hop around for that bit. We also like to incorporate words from the languages spoken by families in our group and each day we pick a different one to sing. We mostly use the words for 'encore' or 'again, again' but you can use the words for 'hello' or anything you choose.

If you're happy and you know it, *clap your hands*,
If you're happy and you know it, *clap your hands*,
If you're happy and you know it,
And your really want to show it,
If you're happy and you know it, *clap your hands*!

If you're happy and you know it, *stamp your feet*...
IIf you're happy and you know it, *do a dance*...
If you're happy and you know it, *pat your head*...
If you're happy and you know it, *touch your nose*...
If you're happy and you know it, shout *'we are!'*

If you're happy and you know it, shout *'encore!'*
If you're happy and you know it, shout *'bravo!'*
If you're happy and you know it, shout *'yatta!'*
If you're happy and you know it, shout *'kedu!'*
If you're happy and you know it, shout *'arís!'*
If you're happy and you know it, shout *'powtórz!'*

Peek a Boo!

When we sing peek-a-boo! songs with young babies, we use transparent scarves just so we don't scare any little ones who are not quite ready for hiding yet. Once your baby is a little older and begins to enjoy hiding, you can use an opaque scarf, or baby's blanket.

I'm hiding, I'm hiding - peek-a-boo! peek-a-boo!
I'm hiding, I'm hiding - peek-a-peek-a boo!
I see you, I see you - peek-a-boo! peek-a-boo!
I see you, I see you - peek-a-peek-a boo!

Shake the Sillies out!

We're going to *shake, shake, shake*, the sillies out!
Shake, shake, shake, the sillies out!
Shake, shake, shake, the sillies out!
Wiggle our troubles away!

We're going to *clap, clap, clap*, the sillies out...
We're going to *stretch, stretch, stretch*, the sillies out...

Rolly Polly

When I was first asked to start a Baby Club I realised that all of the baby songs I knew were in Irish, even though Irish has not been spoken in my family for many generations. It struck me that we all learn baby songs in our first language – so I include this Irish one in our sessions to remind me. It's a really easy one to translate into other languages – we also sing it in French and Urdu!

Rolly polly, rolly polly – suas! suas! suas!
Rolly polly, rolly polly – sias! sias! sias!
Rolly polly, rolly polly – amach! amach! amach!
Rolly polly, rolly polly – isteach! isteach! isteach!

Rolly polly, rolly polly – stretch up high!
Rolly polly, rolly polly – way down low!
Rolly polly, rolly polly – arms out wide!
Rolly polly, rolly polly – hugs in tight!

French:
Rolly polly, rolly polly – en haut! en haut! en haut!
Rolly polly, rolly polly – en bas! en bas! en bas!
Rolly polly, rolly polly – ouvre! ouvre! ouvre!
Rolly polly, rolly polly – ferme! ferme! ferme!

Urdu:
Rolly polly, rolly polly – upar! upar! upar!
Rolly polly, rolly polly – neechay! neechay! neechay!
Rolly polly, rolly polly – baahir! baahir! baahir!
Rolly polly, rolly polly – andar! andar! andar!